Ludwig van Beethoven

Symphony No. 2 in D major / D-Dur

Op. 36

Edited by / Herausgegeben von
Richard Clarke

EULENBURG

EAS 186
ISBN 978-3-7957-6586-6
ISMN 979-0-2002-2616-4

© 2014 Ernst Eulenburg & Co GmbH, Mainz
for Europe excluding the British Isles
Ernst Eulenburg Ltd, London
for all other countries
CD ℗ 2003 NAXOS Rights US, Inc.
CD © 2014 Ernst Eulenburg Ltd, London

Ernst Eulenburg Ltd
48 Great Marlborough Street
London W1F 7BB

Contents / Inhalt

Allegro con brio

Preface

Dedicated to Prince Carl von Lichnowsky
Composed: 1802/03 in Vienna and Heiligenstadt
First performance: 5 April 1803 in Vienna,
conducted by Ludwig van Beethoven
Original publisher: Kunst- und Industriekontor, Vienna, 1804
Versions and arrangements: as piano trio Op.38,
arranged by Ferdinand Ries, 1806
Instrumentation: 2 Flutes, 2 Oboes, 2 Clarinets, 2 Bassoons – 2 Horns,
2 Trumpets – Timpani – Strings
Duration: ca. 36 minutes

Mozart was nine years old when he completed his First Symphony (K16); Haydn, somewhat more conventionally, began writing symphonies in his mid-twenties. Beethoven however waited until he was nearly 30 before giving the world his Symphony No.1 (1799–1800). Though it contains some striking features – not least the surprising seventh chord that opens the first movement's slow introduction – it is in broad terms a relatively conventional Classical Era symphony. For the Beethoven commentator Lewis Lockwood, the composer 'played it safe rather than provoke his audience'.[1] The composer Hector Berlioz was even blunter: 'In a word, Beethoven is not here'.[2] Listening to the brilliant Menuetto (by common consent the outstanding movement in the First Symphony) one might find it hard to agree entirely with Berlioz; but certainly there are no formal innovations in the First Symphony to match the highly theatrical integration of slow introduction and sonata form allegro in the first movement of the *Pathétique* Sonata, Op.13 (1799), nor does it approach the expressive heights and depths of the finest of the Op.18 String Quartets (1798–1800).

In both formal daring and emotional content the Second Symphony marks a significant step forward. As in the First Symphony, there is a slow introduction, again marked *Adagio molto*; but while that of the First Symphony lasts a mere 12 bars, this one extends to 33 bars. It is far more adventurous in colour and texture than at any point in the First Symphony; it is also much richer in incident. The opening ceremonial two-note call to attention dovetails twice (bar 1 and bar 5) into the phrases of an eight-bar melody that might well have served as the main theme of a symphonic slow movement. A surprise turn to B flat major (b12) leads to

---

[1] Lewis Lockwood, *Beethoven: the Music and the Life* (New York, 2003), 148
[2] Hector Berlioz, *A Critical Study of Beethoven's Nine Symphonies*, trans. Edwin Evans (Urbana, 2000), 30f

a passage of considerable harmonic tension and uncertainty. Ambiguity is roundly dismissed by a massive *fortissimo* unison figure, which for a moment seems to look forward to the first movement of the Ninth Symphony. After this comes a long, mysterious preparation on the dominant of the home key, but whether this will prove to be major or minor remains at this stage tantalizingly unclear. The model for this dramatic *Adagio molto* is clearly the substantial *Adagio* introduction from Mozart's 'Prague' Symphony (K504), but in this case Beethoven's leading motifs are so sharply memorable and starkly contrasted that the 'introductory' role of this section is called into question.

Subtleties and surprises abound in the following *Allegro con brio*. The first theme is introduced, not by treble instruments (as was customary at the time) but by lower strings. The bass theme is moreover, intriguingly incomplete – in fact what seems to be a counter melody on oboe and bassoon (b41) quickly takes over the main melodic role to lead to the first *forte* (b47). Striking too is the momentum generated by these ideas, sustained through a wealth of dramatic, often rapid contrast. Tension continues to accumulate until it explodes in the first movement coda, with its thrilling long chromatic ascent in bb326–336.

Where the second movement of the First Symphony was a light and playful *Andante*, that of the Second is a true lyrical slow movement, marked *Larghetto*. Tovey described it as 'one of the most luxurious slow movements in the world'.[3] Schubert was so impressed that he imitated it in several of his own slow movements, notably that of the quasi-symphonic *Grand Duo*, D813. Aside from its two eminently singable main themes, the movement abounds in memorable touches of instrumental colour: the fusion of clarinets and bassoons in the first theme, the wind-string dialogues in bb66–70, the yodelling horns in bb89–93.

If the Scherzo (the first time Beethoven used this designation in a symphony) is less of an advance on the First Symphony's racing, widely modulating Menuetto, the *Allegro molto* finale is something else entirely. The energy and momentum are even more striking than in the first movement, the motivic springboard here being an abruptly leaping figure on the dominant, full of compressed rhythmic energy. The more the movement progresses, the more the surprises accumulate: sudden halts, ruptures in texture and rhythmic continuity, and dislocating harmonic changes (see bb334–337, 366–373, 414–415). In Classical Era symphonies the first movement was usually the weightiest, but in the Second Symphony the finale's proportionally immense coda (bb282–442) caps the entire work, as though everything had been leading up to it. After this there could be no turning back to the relative safety of the First Symphony: from now on Beethoven's audiences must keep pace with him.

Stephen Johnson

---

[3] Donald Francis Tovey, *Essays in Musical Analysis*, Vol.1 (London, 1935), 27

Vorwort

dem Fürsten Carl von Lichnowsky gewidmet
komponiert: 1802/1803 in Wien und Heiligenstadt
Uraufführung: 5. April 1803 in Wien unter der Leitung Beethovens
Originalverlag: Kunst- und Industriekontor, Wien, 1804
Fassungen und Bearbeitungen: als Klaviertrio op. 38 arrangiert von
Ferdinand Ries, 1806
Orchesterbesetzung: 2 Flöten, 2 Oboen, 2 Klarinetten, 2 Fagotte –
2 Hörner, 2 Trompeten – Pauken – Streicher
Spieldauer: etwa 36 Minuten

Mozart vollendete seine erste Sinfonie (KV 16) im Alter von neun Jahren, Haydn begann seine ersten Sinfonien mit Mitte 20 zu schreiben. Beethoven jedoch wartete, bis er fast 30 Jahre alt war, ehe er der Welt seine Sinfonie Nr. 1 (1799–1800) präsentierte. Obwohl sie einige herausragende Merkmale aufweist – nicht zuletzt den überraschenden Septakkord, der die langsame Einleitung des 1. Satzes eröffnet –, handelt es sich im Großen und Ganzen um eine relativ traditionelle klassische Sinfonie. Für den Beethoven-Kommentator Lewis Lockwood „schlug sich Beethoven lieber auf die sichere Seite, anstatt zu provozieren […]".[1] Der Komponist Hector Berlioz äußerte sich sogar noch deutlicher: „Mit einem Worte: Das ist nicht Beethoven".[2] Beim Hören des brillanten Menuetto (nach allgemeiner Auffassung der bemerkenswerteste Satz der 1. Sinfonie) mag es schwer erscheinen, einer Meinung mit Berlioz zu sein. Die 1. Sinfonie hat jedoch keine formalen Neuerungen, die sich mit der höchst theatralischen Kombination der langsamen Einleitung und der Allegro-Sonatenform aus dem ersten Satz der *Pathétique*-Sonate, op. 13 (1799), vergleichen lassen; und sie reicht auch nicht an die ausdrucksvollen Höhen und Tiefen des besten Streichquartetts aus seinem Opus 18 (1798–1800) heran.

Sowohl hinsichtlich der formalen Kühnheit als auch des emotionalen Gehalts markiert die 2. Sinfonie einen deutlichen Schritt nach vorne. Sie hat wie die Sinfonie Nr. 1 eine langsame, ebenfalls mit Adagio molto bezeichnete Einleitung. Während aber die Einleitung der ersten Sinfonie nur 12 Takte dauert, ist die der 2. Sinfonie 33 Takte lang. Die 2. Sinfonie ist von den Klangfarben und der Struktur her viel gewagter als die 1. Sinfonie und sie ist auch

---

[1] Lewis Lockwood: *Beethoven. Seine Musik. Sein Leben*, Kassel 2009, S. 115.
[2] Hector Berlioz: *A Critical Study of Beethoven's Nine Symphonies*, Übersetzung von Edwin Evans, Urbana 2000, S. 30f.

wesentlich ereignisreicher. Der feierliche, aus zwei Noten bestehende Eröffnungsruf passt zweimal (Takt 1 und Takt 5) zu den Phrasen einer achttaktigen Melodie, die auch gut als Hauptthema für den langsamen Satz einer Sinfonie hätte dienen können. Eine überraschende Wendung in B-Dur (Takt 12) führt in einen Abschnitt mit einer deutlichen harmonischen Spannung und Ungewissheit. Diese Unklarheit verschwindet durch eine gewaltige Unisono-Figur im Fortissimo, die für einen Moment scheinbar den ersten Satz der 9. Sinfonie erahnen lässt. Hiernach folgt eine lange, geheimnisvolle Vorbereitung in der Dominante der Anfangs-tonart, aber ob sich dies als Dur oder Moll erweisen wird, bleibt zu diesem Zeitpunkt unklar. Vorbild für dieses dramatische Adagio molto ist zweifellos die bedeutende Adagio-Einleitung von Mozarts *Prager* Sinfonie (KV 504), aber in diesem Fall sind Beethovens Motive so einprägsam und kontrastreich, dass die „einleitende" Funktion dieses Abschnitts in Frage gestellt wird.

Das folgende Allegro con brio wartet mit zahlreichen Feinheiten und Überraschungen auf. Das erste Thema wird nicht von den Melodieinstrumenten eingeführt, wie es zu jener Zeit üblich war, sondern von tiefen Streichern. Das Bassthema ist interessanterweise zudem unvollständig – was eigentlich eine Gegenmelodie in der Oboe und dem Fagott zu sein scheint (Takt 41), übernimmt bald die Rolle der Hauptmelodie und führt zum ersten Forte (Takt 47). Auffallend ist auch die Impulskraft, die durch diese Ideen erzeugt wird und die durch vielerlei dramatische, oftmals schnelle Kontraste aufrechterhalten wird. Die Spannung baut sich weiter auf, bis sie in der Coda des ersten Satzes mit dem langen, aufregenden chromatischen Aufstieg in den Takten 326–336 explodiert.

Während der zweite Satz der ersten Sinfonie ein leichtes und spielerisches Andante war, ist der zweite Satz in der Sinfonie Nr. 2 ein sehr lyrischer langsamer Satz mit der Bezeichnung Larghetto. Tovey beschrieb ihn als „einen der luxuriösesten langsamen Sätze der Welt".[3] Schubert war so beeindruckt, dass er ihn in einigen seiner langsamen Sätze imitierte, ins-besondere in seinem quasi-sinfonischen *Grand Duo*, D813. Abgesehen von den beiden über-aus sangbaren Hauptthemen ist der Satz von einem unvergleichlichen Gespür für instru-mentale Klangfarben geprägt: die Verschmelzung der Klarinetten und Fagotte im ersten Thema, der Dialog zwischen den Bläsern und Streichern in den Takten 66–70 und die jodelnden Hörner in den Takten 89–93.

Auch wenn das Scherzo (Beethoven verwendete diese Bezeichnung hier zum ersten Mal in einer Sinfonie) im Vergleich zum gehetzten modulierten Menuetto der ersten Sinfonie keinen großen Fortschritt darstellt, so ist das Finale Allegro molto völlig anders. Die Energie und die Impulskraft sind noch auffallender als im ersten Satz, da das motivische Sprungbrett hier eine plötzlich in die Dominante springende Figur ist, die voller komprimierter rhyth-mischer Energie steckt. Je mehr der Satz voranschreitet, desto mehr Überraschungen häufen sich: plötzliche Pausen, Brüche in der Struktur und rhythmischen Kontinuität und ver-schobene harmonische Wechsel (siehe Takte 334–337, 366–373, 414–415). In den Sinfonien

---

[3] Donald Francis Tovey: *Essays in Musical Analysis*, Bd. 1, London 1935, S. 27.

IX

der Klassik war der erste Satz normalerweise der wichtigste, aber in Beethovens 2. Sinfonie übertrifft die verhältnismäßig gewaltige Coda des Finales (Takte 282–442) das gesamte Werk, als ob alles zu ihr hingeführt hätte. Hiernach konnte es kein Zurück mehr zu der relativen Sicherheit in der ersten Sinfonie geben: Von nun an musste Beethovens Publikum mit ihm Schritt halten.

Stephen Johnson
Übersetzung: Uta Pastowski

Symphony No. 2

À son Altesse Monseigneur le Prince Charles de Lichnowsky

Ludwig van Beethoven
(1770–1827)
Op. 36

EAS 186

Edited by Richard Clarke
© 2014 Ernst Eulenburg Ltd, London
and Ernst Eulenburg & Co GmbH, Mainz

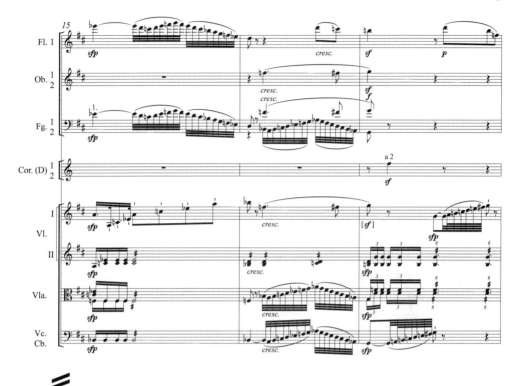

4

9

14

16

19

24

27

EAS 186

29

EAS 186

30

32

II. Larghetto (♪ = 92)

42

44

III. Scherzo

Allegro ($\downarrow$. = 100)

52

54

Scherzo da capo

IV. Allegro molto (♩ = 152)

58

60

62

74

EAS 186